Who F*rted This Time?

ANGUS
& ROBERTSON
PUBLISHERS

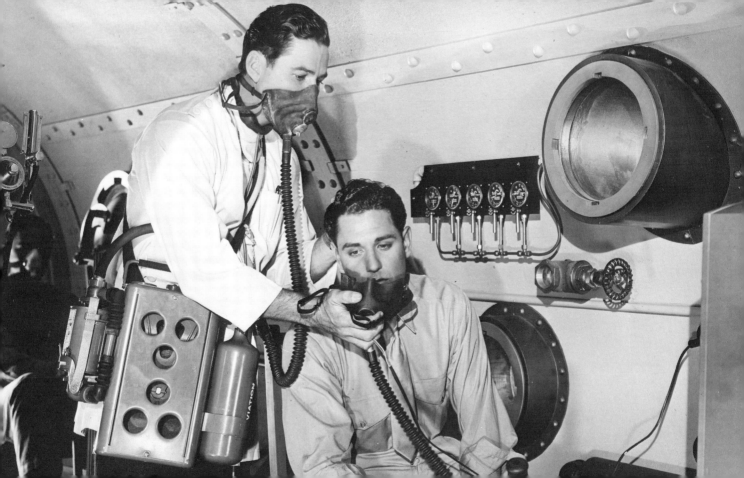

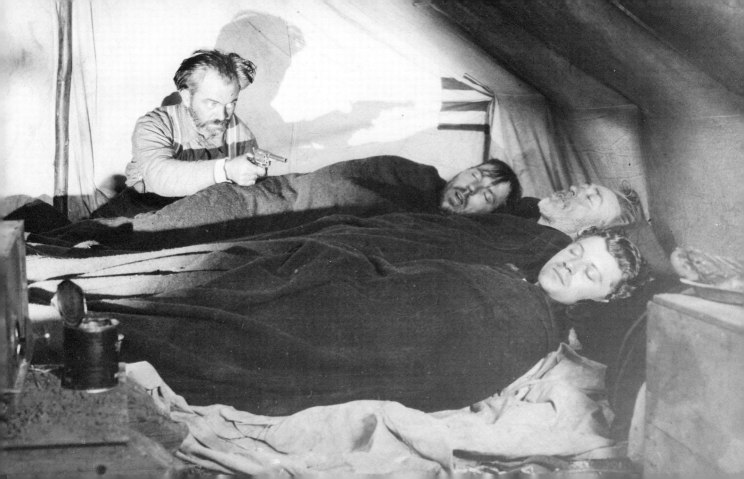

EIN VOLK
EIN REICH
EIN FUEHRER

ANGUS & ROBERTSON PUBLISHERS

Unit 4, Eden Park, 31 Waterloo Road,
North Ryde, NSW, Australia 2113, and
16 Golden Square, London W1R 4BN,
United Kingdom

First published in Australia
by Angus & Robertson Publishers in 1987
First published in the United Kingdom
by Angus & Robertson (UK) in 1987
Reprinted 1987, 1989, 1991

Copyright © Philip Cammarata 1987

ISBN 0 207 15391 4

Printed and Bound in Great Britain
by Courier International Limited, East Kilbride